GROWING

Senior Authors
Carl B. Smith
Ronald Wardhaugh

Macmillan Publishing Co., Inc.
New York
Collier Macmillan Publishers
London

SERIES r
Macmillan Reading

1

This work is also published together with other works in a single volume under the title: *Rhymes and Reasons* copyright © 1980 Macmillan Publishing Co., Inc. Parts of this work were published in SERIES r: The New Macmillan Reading Program.

Macmillan Publishing Co., Inc.
866 Third Avenue, New York, New York 10022
Collier Macmillan Canada, Ltd.

Printed in the United States of America
ISBN 0-02-128790-2
987654321

ACKNOWLEDGMENTS

The publisher gratefully acknowledges permission to reprint the following copyrighted material:

"Davy Crockett," adapted from *Davy Crockett: Young Rifleman* by Aileen Wells Parks. Copyright © 1949, 1962 by The Bobbs-Merrill Company, Inc. Reprinted by permission of the publisher.

"Growing Up Chinese-American," from *Chinatown Sunday* by Carol Ann Bales. Copyright © 1973. Reprinted with the permission of Contemporary Books, Inc.

"The Medal," from *Shoeshine Girl* by Clyde Robert Bulla. Copyright © 1975 by Clyde Robert Bulla. By permission of Thomas Y. Crowell and Curtis Brown, Ltd.

"A New Song," adapted from the book *The Waterless Mountain* by Laura Adams Armer. Copyright © 1933 by Longmans, Green and Co. Copyright © 1959 by Laura Adams Armer, published by the David McKay Co., Inc. Reprinted by permission of the publisher.

"No One Else," by Elaine Laron from *Free to Be . . . You and Me,* published by McGraw-Hill. Copyright © 1974 by Free To Be Foundation, Inc.

"Phillis Wheatley," adapted from *Phillis Wheatley: Young Colonial Poet* by Kathryn Kilby Borland and Helen Ross Speicher. Copyright © 1968 by The Bobbs-Merrill Company, Inc. Reprinted by permission of the publisher.

"The Shoeshine Chair," adapted from Chapter 10 of *Angie* by Janice May Udry. Copyright © 1971 by Janice May Udry. By permission of Harper & Row, Publishers, Inc.

"Trina and Maggie," adapted from *Trina's Boxcar* by Patricia Miles Martin. Copyright © 1967 by Abingdon Press. Used by permission.

"The Tuesday Elephant," adapted from *The Tuesday Elephant* by Nancy Garfield. Copyright © 1968 by Nancy Garfield. By permission of Thomas Y. Crowell and author, and Agents, Raines and Raines.

"Who's Afraid?" reprinted from *Oodles of Noodles* by Lucia M. and James L. Hymes, Jr. Copyright © 1966 by Lucia M. and James L. Hymes, Jr. A Young Scott Book, reprinted by permission of Addison-Wesley Publishing Company.

Illustrations: Ray Cruz, pp. 4-7; John Wallner, pp. 10-16; Diane and Leo Dillon, pp. 18-27; Dora Leder, pp. 28-38; Tony Chen, pp. 50-55; Joel Snyder, pp. 56-64; Bill Smith, p. 65; Jerry Pinkney, pp. 68-79; Mila Lazarevich, pp. 80-90; Jan Pyk, pp. 91, 39, 17; Albert John Pucci, pp. 92-100; Melinda May, p. 101. **Photographs:** Carol Ann Bales, pp. 44-49. **Cover Design:** AKM Associates

4

Contents

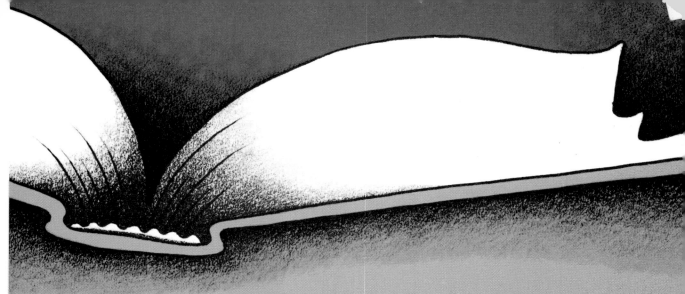

GROWING

Growing is something you do all the time. It's both exciting and a little scary. But it's something everyone does. Learning about new things and meeting new people helps you to grow. Learning to understand your own feelings and the feelings of others helps you to grow, too.

In "Growing," you will read about young people having experiences that help them to learn and to grow. The people you will meet will take you on some exciting adventures. You will visit Boston in the days before the American Revolution. You will meet elephants in the African jungle. You will ride horseback with some Navaho friends. You will be in the woods with a young boy as he struggles to escape from an angry bear.

As you read, think about how different people face the problems and excitement of growing. What does growing mean for each of them? What does it mean for you?

The Medal

Clyde Robert Bulla

Sarah Ida Becker was staying with her Aunt Claudia for the summer and was determined to find a job to earn some spending money. Al Winkler, the owner of a shoeshine stand, was the only person who would hire a young girl without experience. Sarah Ida accepted the job.

Every evening after work, Sarah Ida was tired. But every morning she was ready to go back to Shoeshine Corner. It wasn't that she liked shining shoes, but things happened at the shoeshine stand. Every customer was different. Every day she found out something new.

Some things she learned by herself—like how much polish to use on a shoe. A thin coat gave a better and quicker shine. Some things Al told her. "When a customer comes here, he gets more than a shine," he said. "He gets to rest in a chair. When you rub with the cloth, it feels good on his feet. When you tie his shoelaces a little tighter, it makes his shoes fit better. My customers go away feeling a little better. Anyway, I *hope* they do."

One warm, cloudy afternoon, he said, "We might as well close up."

"Why?" she asked. "It's only three o'clock."

"It's going to rain. Nobody gets a shine on a rainy day."

He began to put away the brushes and shoe polish. She helped him.

"Maybe you can run home before the rain," he said. A few big drops splashed on the sidewalk. "No. Too late now."

They sat under the little roof, out of the rain.

"Hear that sound?" he said. "Every time I hear rain on a tin roof, I get to thinking about when I was a boy. We lived in an old truck

with a tin roof over the back."

"You *lived* in a truck?"

"Most of the time. We slept under the tin roof, and when it rained, the sound put me to sleep. We went all over the South in that truck."

"You and your mother and father?"

"My dad and I."

"What were you doing, driving all over the South?"

"My dad sold medicine."

"What kind?"

"Something to make you strong and keep you from getting sick."

"Did you take it?"

"No. I guess it wasn't any good."

She had never before heard him talk much about himself. She wanted him to go on.

"Was it fun living in a truck?"

"Fun? I wouldn't say so. Riding along was all right. Sometimes my dad and I stopped close to the woods, and that was all right, too. But I never liked it when we were in town selling medicine. Dad would play the mouth harp, and he made me sing. He wanted me to dance a jig, too, but I never could."

She tried to imagine Al as a little boy. She couldn't at all. "Why did he want you to sing and dance?" she asked.

"To draw a crowd. When there was a crowd, he sold medicine. We didn't stay anywhere very long—except once. We stayed in one place six months. My dad did farm work, and I went to school."

He told her about the school. It was just outside a town. The teacher was Miss Miller. The schoolhouse had only one room.

"There was this big stove," he said, "and that winter I kept the fire going. Miss Miller never had to carry coal when I was there."

"Did you like her?" asked Sarah Ida. "Was she a good teacher?"

"Best teacher I ever had. Of course, she was just about the *only* one. I hadn't been to school much, but she took time to show me things. Do teachers still give medals in school?"

"Sometimes. Not very often."

"Miss Miller gave medals. They were all alike. Every one had a star on it. At the end of school you got one

if you were the best in reading or
spelling or writing or whatever it was.
Everybody wanted a medal, but I knew I'd never
get one because I wasn't the best in anything. And
at the end of school, you know what happened?"

"What?"

"She called my name. The others all thought
it was a joke. But she wasn't laughing. She said,
'Al wins a medal for building the best fires.'"

"And it *wasn't* a joke?" asked Sarah Ida.

"No. She gave me a medal. One of the big
boys said, 'You better keep that, Al, because it's
the only one you'll ever get.'"

"And did you keep it?" He held up his watch
chain. Something was hanging from it—something
that looked like a worn, old coin.

"That's what you won?" asked Sarah Ida.

He nodded.

"That's a medal?" she said. "That little old
piece of tin?"

She shouldn't have said it. As soon as the words were out, she was sorry.

Al sat very still. He looked into the street. A moment before, he had been a friend. Now he was a stranger.

He said, "Rain's stopped—for a while anyway."

He slid out of his chair. She got up, too. "I—" she began.

He dragged the folding door across the stand and locked up.

"Go on. Run," he said. "Maybe you can get home before the rain starts again."

She stood there. "I didn't mean what you think I did," she said. "That medal—it doesn't matter if it's tin or silver or gold. It doesn't matter *what* it's made of, if it's something you like. I said the wrong thing, but it wasn't what I *meant*. I—" He had his back to her. She didn't think he was listening. She said, "*Listen* to me!"

He turned around. "You like ice cream?"

"Yes," she said.

"Come on. I'll buy you a cone."

She went with him, around the corner to Pearl's Ice Cream Shack.

"What kind?" he asked.

"Chocolate," she said.

They sat on a bench inside the Shack and ate their chocolate cones.

"It's raining again," he said.

"Yes," she said.

Then they were quiet, while they listened to the rain. And she was happy because the stranger was gone and Al was back.

Later that summer, Sarah Ida faced a problem. Al was hit by a car and had to stay in the hospital. Sarah Ida wanted to keep the stand open by herself, but she was not sure she could do it. To find out what she did and what she learned during that important summer in her life, read The Shoeshine Girl *by Clyde Robert Bulla.*

Who's Afraid?

I went to sleep last night
  And dreamed.
They tell me that I woke
  And screamed.
I was not really scared.
  Not me!
I simply called so they
  Could see
The witch who leaped up from
  The floor
And flew right through my
  Bedroom door.
If she should come again
  Tonight,
I'll scream again with all
  My might
But just so they can come
  And see
And not because I'm scared—
  Not me!

—Lucia and James L. Hymes, Jr.

17

DAVY CROCKETT

Aileen Wells Parks

Davy Crockett was lonesome. It was a sunny day in early summer, and Pa had given all the other boys jobs to do.

Ma, Janie, and Polly were working, too. And baby Sarah and little Joe were sound asleep.

Davy wandered up the hill. A big hound was lying half in the shade, half in the sun. Davy called, "Here, Whirlwind, here. Come here, Whirly."

The dog cocked one ear and looked around lazily. He did not get up. He didn't even stretch.

"Best bear dog in all the Great Smoky Mountains," Pa often said. "Give me old Whirlwind, and I can tree any bear that ever grew. He has more sense than most men."

"Come on, Whirlwind. Get up." Davy pulled the dog's ear. "Let's go hunt bear."

Whirlwind growled softly. He might have been dreaming.

Davy poked at him. "Bear, Whirlwind. Bear!" He tried to make his voice deep like his father's voice, but he was not successful.

This time Whirlwind got up and stretched. He did not jump around and bark as he did when Pa said, "Bear!"

Davy started up the path toward the forest. Whirlwind followed. He looked slow and lazy, but he kept up with the boy. Davy talked to him.

"We'll go right up this path. Then we come to the trail. Bill showed me one time. It starts at the big sycamore tree where Pa got the wildcat."

Whirlwind yawned loudly. Davy looked back. The hound seemed ready to stop and finish his nap.

"Come on, Whirlwind. Here, boy, here!" Davy picked up a stick, held it before the dog, and then threw it up the path as hard as he could throw.

Whirlwind looked at him with scorn. That was puppy play.

Then Davy remembered. He would need a stick in case he met a bear. Looking for a good strong stick, he left the path. Soon he found a kind of trail which led like a tunnel through the underbrush.

It was fun to go through the tunnel. It turned first to the right and then to the left. Sometimes sunlight came through the leaves. Sometimes the tunnel was almost dark. Davy forgot he was looking for a stick. He pretended that he was a fox trailing an opossum.

His bare feet made no noise on the path. He brushed the little branches away from his face as quietly as he could. Often the tunnel was so low he had to crawl.

After a long time he came out beside a rocky ledge. Davy climbed up and lay down to rest. He watched the sun on the leaves over his head. Then he fell sound asleep.

When he woke up he thought Wilson was pushing him out of their bed. He kicked back. His foot hit soft fur. Since he slept under a fur covering all winter long, that felt right.

Then something cold touched his face. Davy threw up his hand and hit the rug again, but this time the rug felt different. Davy opened his eyes and looked behind him.

A little bear cub was sitting quietly on the rock beside him.

The bear seemed friendly. It wrinkled up its nose and sniffed at Davy. It looked at him out of bright black eyes. Then it put its nose down on his hand.

It was a cold nose and Davy jumped. When he suddenly sat up, the cub moved back. It was such a cute little thing scuttling away on all fours that Davy laughed.

The cub must have liked the sound of Davy's laugh. It stopped and turned to look back.

Davy held out his hand. "I bet I could make a pet out of you," he said.

The little bear wrinkled its nose at him again. Then it sat down and watched Davy. The boy got to his feet to go over to it.

Just as he moved, Davy heard a snort. It was a scary sort of sound. Davy stood very still. He did not dare even to look around.

There was another snort. This time Davy looked up. A large brown bear was watching him out of little, beady eyes. Its mouth was open. Its big red tongue hung out.

The sight surprised Davy so much that he screamed. He looked around to find a place to run. The only open space he could see was across the rocky ledge. There were big trees on the other side with few bushes under them.

Davy tried to slip away. The big bear started moving, too. Davy was watching so closely he slipped on some loose gravel. He grabbed up a handful of the small pebbles and flung them straight at the two bears.

The mother might have caught him then, but the little bear whimpered. The big bear stopped quickly and went to her baby.

Davy, on one knee, saw the mother nuzzle the little bear. He jumped up and ran. Under the trees he turned to look back. The mother bear was watching him. She was in front of the cub.

Davy did want that cub for a pet. "I could call him Bear Hug," he thought.

The bear must have understood. She glared and growled and then took a step forward. "G-r-r-r," the bear said again. She stretched out a forepaw and raked her claws over the rock. The claws were like a cat's, but they were bigger and longer. The scratch left white gashes on the rock.

Davy kept his eye on the bear but began backing down the hill. That growl had made his heart beat fast. Then he stepped on a branch which crackled loudly.

The sound startled the bear, and she moved toward the boy. Not even her baby's tiny growl stopped her this time. She was headed straight for Davy.

Davy turned and ran as fast as he could go.

The woods were clear, and the way was slightly downhill. But the big bear, growling deep in her throat, ran faster than Davy could.

Davy felt a scream burst from his throat. Then he closed his mouth tight to keep all his breath for running.

He could hear the bear behind him. He fell and rolled over and over down a steep place on the hill.

The bear was running very fast. She went right past where Davy lay. But she did not go far. She turned. And Davy saw her beady eyes, red now with anger, as she came toward him.

Suddenly there was a great barking. The bear turned its head, then its whole body, to face this unexpected sound.

It was Whirlwind. The dog was making enough noise for a whole pack of bearhounds. He jumped from side to side of the angry bear. He barked right in her face but kept out of reach of her powerful paws. Her long claws were bared as she grabbed for the dog.

By circling, Whirlwind forced the bear to
retreat. When the bear moved toward Davy, the
dog dashed forward to nip her.

Davy was too scared to move.

The dog would circle toward one side. And
the bear would circle facing him. When he was
even with her and threatening to go past, she
would growl and attack. As Whirlwind raced
around to the other side, she moved back.

Davy looked up the hill. There was the cub, watching with as much interest as Davy.

The mother also saw the cub. She began backing steadily up the hill. Her angry eyes watched Whirlwind. But she did not try to attack him now. The hound kept up a great fury of barking and running. But he was not pressing the attack as hard as he had at first.

Finally the mother bear reached her cub. She and the dog stood growling threats at each other.

Suddenly the two bears were gone in the leafy forest. Davy was amazed that they could disappear so fast.

Whirlwind came back and stood by the boy. He was panting hard.

Just then Mr. Crockett came up the hill. His rifle was ready in his hands. "Davy! Davy!" he was shouting.

"Here I am, Pa!" Davy called.

"You all right, Davy?"

"Pa, you should have seen old Whirlwind drive that bear back up that hill!" Davy forgot he had ever been scared. "Pa, will you give Whirlwind to me for my bearhound?"

Mr. Crockett studied the boy. "When you get big enough to hunt bear, you may have him for your very own," he promised.

TRINA & MAGGIE

Patricia Miles Martin

Words are very important to friends, as you will see when you read this story. Trina is a Mexican-American who has just moved with her parents and older sister, Carla, to a little Wyoming town. More than anything else, Trina wants to be friends with Maggie, a girl at school. Maggie wants to be Trina's friend, too. When Trina speaks Spanish, her words flow out. But when she tries to talk to Maggie in English, nothing comes out right.

Trina went to school. Every night Mama held the reader and listened while she read.

Papa listened, too. Trina spoke words and more words. But she was still shy and unsure of herself with Maggie and the older girls.

In school, she read through the first reader and part of the way through the second. She read slowly. But she read well.

One Friday after school, Maggie spoke to Trina and Carla. "Tomorrow's my birthday. I'm having a party. I'd like it if you two would come."

"It will be at two o'clock tomorrow," Maggie said. "Charlie Wilson is coming and Abner Marshall and all the others."

Trina looked at Maggie. Friendship. She would be a friend to Maggie. She swallowed hard and spoke in English, "I-like-you."

Everyone laughed except Trina. She felt hot with her embarrassment. She could hardly believe that Maggie was laughing at her.

"No voy a tu fiesta," Trina said.

"She says she won't come to your party," Carla said. She shrugged her shoulders. "I guess she doesn't want to go. I'll go, I guess."

Trina told her mother what had happened.

How wonderful it was to tell her troubles to Mama in Spanish. How wonderful to speak Spanish together. It was a beautiful, beautiful language. At the moment, Trina didn't care if she ever spoke English.

"Well," Mama said, "they are at fault. You are not. Sometimes boys and girls do not know how to accept a compliment with grace. Perhaps until they learn this, you will *show* that you like people rather than tell them."

"But I do not like Maggie now," Trina said. "Perhaps I hate her. I am not quite sure."

"You will never have friends if you expect them to be without fault," Mama said.

That evening their mother ironed a red dress for Carla. She reached for a white dress and laid it over the ironing board.

"I am not going to the party, Mama," Trina said.

"You have not yet forgiven Maggie?" her mother asked.

"No, Mama."

"Very well. You need not go, of course. But you may feel differently tomorrow. You will take presents when you go."

"What presents?" Trina asked.

Their mother set the iron on the stove. "Let me think." She lifted the lid of the linen chest. "Perhaps we might make a doll's dress. Maggie will have a doll like your Ana Maria on her birthday.

I was in the store when her father bought it—the doll in the glass counter."

She shook out a short length of red material sprigged with tiny yellow flowers. "See. I have saved this material. Now we will measure your Ana Maria. We will make a dress for Maggie's new doll. We will start at once."

"But if I do not go to the party?"

"You could then have a beautiful dress that will fit Ana Maria. This is for you to decide."

While they talked, Carla said, "I will buy a present for Maggie. I'll stop at the store and get something on the way to the party."

She reached on the shelf for a baking powder can that held coins she had saved. She twisted off the top and emptied the coins on the

table. She brushed half of them into the palm of her left hand and slid them into her pocket. Then she put the rest of the coins back into the can and twisted the top tightly shut.

"What will you buy?" Trina asked.

"A surprise," said Carla.

Mama and Trina measured and cut and sewed to make a dress to fit a doll.

The next afternoon Carla dressed for the party.

Trina looked at her white dress, crisp with Mama's starch. It would be beautiful with her red sash. She remembered Maggie's laughter. "I can't go," she said to her mother.

"Very well," Mama said. "And the present for Maggie? Do you choose to give this?"

"Yes. I choose to give it. I will send it with Carla," Trina said.

She watched the girls and boys going up the hill to Maggie's house.

That afternoon, Mama made hot chocolate, and they each had a sweet roll with it. Even so, the time dragged until Carla came home. The afternoon was so long.

"But I am not sorry I stayed home, Mama. I couldn't have gone."

"I understand," Mama said.

When Carla came home, she took off her red dress and put on her jeans and her blue and yellow shirt.

"Everything happened at that party," Carla said. "It was fun. The birthday cake fell off the table, and if it hadn't been for me, Maggie wouldn't have had any candles to blow out."

'What do you mean?" Mama asked.

"Well, after the cake fell, I picked up the candles and put them on my present," Carla said.

"What was your present?" Trina asked.

"Gumdrops," said Carla. "I put a candle on each gumdrop. It was as good as a cake. Mrs. Tolley lighted them, and Maggie made a wish and blew them out."

"What did Maggie wish?" Trina asked.

"How could I know?" Carla asked. "When you blow out candles and make a wish, you don't tell what it is."

"And the doll's dress?" Trina asked. "What did Maggie say when she saw it?"

"I don't remember," Carla said.

The next day at school, Maggie walked straight to Trina.

"Trina, thank you for the doll's dress. It's the prettiest

dress I ever saw. It fits my doll.'' She pushed her red braids over her shoulders, and the dimples came in her cheeks. *"Trina, me gusta,"* she said.

Everybody laughed, even Trina. Maggie, too.

"I sound funny," Maggie said. "Spanish words are hard. But if you want to, I can try to speak Spanish while you try to speak English."

"You sound funny, Maggie," Carla said.

"I know. Everybody does at first," Maggie said. "Now, I will say 'thank you,' Trina, and you can say 'you're welcome' in English. Now listen, Trina. Say it after me: You-are-welcome."

Trina repeated the words slowly: "Say it after me, you are welcome."

Maggie bent over with laughter.

Trina felt her own face

crinkling. She blinked to keep back the tears.

"Don't pay any attention to her," Carla said.

"*Riense*," Trina said. "*No me importa.*"

"She says she doesn't care if you laugh," Carla said. "She cares."

"Oh, well," Maggie said. "It's not fun to play with her anyway. If I laugh, she cries. And she won't even try to speak English."

Trina didn't stay to watch Maggie go up the hill. On her way home, she kicked the dirt until the air was thick with yellow-red dust.

"Why you are so dirty?" Mama asked pleasantly in English.

"You have it backward, Mama," Trina said in Spanish. "It should be, 'Why-are-you-so-dirty?'"

"Good," said Mama. "One of us is learning English."

Trina did her homework and thought about Maggie. If she wanted Maggie to be a friend, she would have to do more than learn English. She would have to be a friend. She would have to laugh with Maggie.

She laughed out loud.

"Why do you laugh?" Mama asked.

"I am practicing," Trina said.

And suddenly she and Mama laughed together.

The next day Trina went straight to Maggie.

Trina spoke in English. "You are welcome. That is the lesson for yesterday. And I am sorry. This is my lesson for today."

"All right, Trina," Maggie said. "Now you have to teach me how to say 'I'm sorry,' too."

"So easy," said Trina. "I am sorry. *Lo siento.*"

Maggie repeated the words. *"Lo siento."*

THE NAME'S THE SAME

Did you know that you can read many words in other languages besides English? The reason is that a lot of words are spelled the same or almost the same in many languages.

Here are some examples:

English	German	Spanish	French	Italian
sack	sack	saco	sac	sacco
music	musik	musica	musique	musica
fruit	frucht	fruta	fruit	frutto
school	schule	escuela	ecole	scuola
cat	katze	gato	chat	gatto

Now see if you can match the words below that mean the same thing in these five different languages.

English	German	Spanish	French	Italian
name	naturlich	nariz	nez	nome
nose	name	natural	naturel	naso
natural	nase	nombre	nom	naturale

Next you will read two *Peanuts* comic strips by Charles Schulz. These comic strips are popular all over the world. They have been translated into many different languages. Here is how the name of one main character would look in the five languages.

English
Charlie Brown

German	Spanish	French	Italian
Karl Braun	Carlos Moreno	Charles Brun	Carlo Bruno

DID YOU SEE THAT LITTLE GIRL WITH THE RED HAIR WALK BY?

YOU GOT SORT OF NERVOUS WHEN SHE WALKED BY, DIDN'T YOU, CHARLIE BROWN?

11-15

WHAT MAKES YOU THINK I GOT NERVOUS?

YOU TIED YOUR PEANUT BUTTER SANDWICH IN A KNOT!

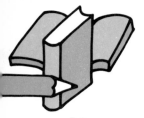

Unlocking New Words

Many words have parts called *prefixes* and *suffixes*. A *prefix* is a word part added to the beginning of a base word. A *suffix* is a word part added to the end of a base word. Knowing the meanings of prefixes and suffixes is very helpful. Sometimes you may see an unfamiliar word. You may not know the meaning of the whole word. But you recognize a prefix or a suffix in the word. Knowing that word part may help you understand the whole word.

Here are some common prefixes and their meanings:

uni-	one, single	**in-**	not
bi-	two, twice	**im-**	not
tri-	three	**non-**	not, without
un-	not	**dis-**	not, the opposite of

ACTIVITY A   Write the answer to each question on your paper.

1. How many colors are there in a <u>tricolor</u> flag?
2. How many wheels does a <u>bicycle</u> have?
3. How many horns does a <u>unicorn</u> have?
4. What are <u>unclean</u> hands?
5. What is <u>impure</u> water?
6. What kind of trip is a <u>nonstop</u> flight?
7. What is <u>invisible</u> ink?

Here are some common suffixes and their meanings:

-or	one whose job is	**-ful**	full of
-er	one whose job is	**-y**	like, full of
-ist	one who works with	**-ly**	like, in the
-less	without		manner of

ACTIVITY B Choose the correct meaning for each word on the left. Write the word and its meaning on your paper.

1. homeless   a. two homes   b. without a home
           c. one who has a full home

2. artist   a. without art   b. full of art
           c. one who works in a form of art

3. thankful   a. full of thanks   b. no thanks
           c. one who has thank-you notes

4. sailor   a. in full sail   b. without a sail
           c. one whose job is sailing

5. icy   a. ice cream   b. full of ice
           c. one who works with ice

ACTIVITY C Write the meaning of the underlined word in each sentence.

1. Kim <u>dislikes</u> snowstorms.
2. Andy watched the <u>painter</u> at work.
3. I'll <u>gladly</u> lend you my extra umbrella.
4. Debbie said the job was <u>impossible</u>.
5. The hot summer sun makes me very <u>thirsty</u>.

Growing Up Chinese-American

Carol Ann Bales

This selection is from a book called Chinatown Sunday. *The book is about Lilliann Der, a ten-year-old girl who lives near Chicago, Illinois. Lilliann's life is like that of many girls her age. She goes to school, takes piano lessons, and belongs to the Girl Scouts. But Lilliann is also Chinese-American, and with her family, she follows many customs of their Chinese heritage.*

Carol Ann Bales, who wrote this selection, is a friend of Lilliann and her family. Ms. Bales taped an interview with each person in the family. She chose the most interesting parts of the tapes to put in her book. That's why Lilliann Der's own words are used to tell you about herself and some of the customs of her family.

One time last summer some kids started asking me: "Are you from China or Japan?" It's pretty hard to explain. I told them I'm not from China or Japan. I was born in Chicago. But I am a Chinese-American.

44

I used to be very shy. I didn't know how to answer questions like that. But after kindergarten I started to talk a lot. I'm in the fifth grade this year. I don't talk so much anymore, but I'm not exactly shy—just sometimes.

My name is Lilliann Der— my American name, that is. My Chinese name is Der Wai Lee. Everyone at home calls me *Lee Lee*, which sounds like Lily. *Lee* means a "little jasmine flower" in Chinese.

My father is assistant manager of the Hong Kong Noodle Company in Chinatown, and we live in Wilmette, a suburb of Chicago.

That's me sitting on the end of the sofa. Then there's Caroline, my older sister, and David, my younger brother. Then there's my father and mother. Vivian and Rosalie, my little sisters, are sitting on my grandmother's lap. We were trying to make Vivian and Rosalie laugh.

On the wall is a picture of my grandfather. He died when I was four. His name was Der Chung. I used to get his pipe for him.

My parents and my grandmother were born in China in a place called Toishan. My grandfather's family lived in China, but I think he was born in the United States. He and some other Chinese men founded the Hong Kong Noodle Company.

My grandma lives with us. She grows Chinese vegetables in our backyard. When she gets up in the morning, she reads for an hour or two in her room, and then she goes outside. Some days she stays out all day.

She planted seventeen or eighteen different kinds of vegetables last summer. She planted Chinese broccoli, *bok choy*—that's Chinese cabbage—mustard greens, string beans, peppers, tomatoes, and three kinds of melons. And she planted some other vegetables that I can't remember.

We ask Grandma's opinion before we do anything that's important, and I always say good morning and good night to her. That's how I show that I love and respect her.

When a baby in our family is one month old, we have a special party. I wore my long dress to the month-old party for my little cousin, Aileen Der. The party was held on the top floor of a restaurant in Chinatown. A lot of people came—about three hundred.

I like month-old parties because of all the food. I do like food. They had bird's nest soup, and they had hard-boiled eggs and ginger, both dyed red, which means "good luck." Those foods were special for the month-old party. We had a lot of other food,

too. We ate with chopsticks. At home we usually use a knife and fork. It's hard to use chopsticks with a plate. A bowl is best.

Before the dinner, Mommy helped pin red carnations on the clothes of Aileen's close relatives. Daddy shook hands, and David and I played string games. There were toasts and speeches. One of Aileen's uncles gave a really funny speech. There are mostly boys in Aileen's family, and so everyone was happy that she turned out to be a girl.

Aileen got a lot of presents and lucky money. Lucky money is money someone gives you in a red envelope.

Aileen wore a special outfit with gold necklaces. Your grandmother on your mother's side always gives you a dress for your month-old party, and both your grandmothers give you necklaces. In China, babies wear an outfit with a hat that has two little ears. The parents hang a little gold figure on the hat. I think that sounds nice.

47

I have one very good school friend. Camille and I met in the second grade, and we've been friends ever since. A few times we broke our friendship, but we made up. It's hard to keep a friendship that long. You find it hard to keep away from an argument. I have other friends, like Robin, and some of them are my relatives.

Camille, Robin, and I all belong to Girl Scouts. Robin's mother is a leader. We go to a meeting one night a week.

I don't have many chores during the school year. I have to practice my piano lessons, but I like to do that. Sometimes when Grandma and Mommy are busy, I feed

Rosalie. We call her *Moy Moy,* which means "little sister". She eats a lot. She's learning to talk. She says words in Chinese unless they're easier to say in English.

Of all the holidays, Christmas is my favorite. Halloween is my second favorite. I guess I like the Moon Festival—because I like to eat moon cakes—and the Chinese New Year best of the Chinese holidays.

These are the things that remind me of the Chinese New Year. The house smells like flowers because Grandma puts narcissus bulbs in water to bloom for New Year's Day. We each get a new outfit. This year Grandma made Mommy, Caroline, Vivian, and me new pants suits. And we make Chinese pastry.

You have to make pastry because you visit your friends and relatives on the Chinese New Year—or they visit you—and you want to have pastry to give to them. We make egg rolls and pastry called *ham gok, tim gok,* and *lor bok go* in Chinese. We always put two tangerines in boxes of pastry for friends. That's for good luck.

In Chinatown there's always a big celebration on the Sunday closest to the Chinese New Year. It's fun. It's also noisy—and crowded. You hear a lot of firecrackers, and I mean a lot, and people stand in the streets to watch the lion dance.

Chinese New Year comes about a month after the January 1 New Year's Day because the Chinese calendar is different from the calendar used in this country. My grandma says we are a year older not just on our birthdays, but on Chinese New Year's Day, too. She says the Chinese New Year is important because it is the time of the year to make plans for the future.

I made three resolutions for this year: to be more patient, to be less shy, and—I forgot the other one.

The Emperor's Nightingale

Hans Christian Andersen

Many years ago, there was an Emperor who lived in the most splendid palace in the most beautiful city in China. Everything in the palace was made of delicate porcelain. Outside, near the palace, the loveliest flowers grew in a very large garden.

Deep in this very large garden was a forest of tall trees and clear, blue lakes. The forest stretched for many miles, and in it lived a Nightingale. From its home in the forest, the Nightingale sang so sweetly that everyone who heard it would stop what they were doing. They would listen to the song, and all would say the same thing: "What a beautiful song!"

Now the Emperor was very proud of his city, his palace, and his garden, and he was greatly pleased when travelers came from everywhere to admire them. These travelers, when they returned home, wrote many books and poems about the magnificent city, the porcelain palace, the lovely garden, and the Nightingale that sang so beautifully.

People all over the world had read the books and poems, but the Emperor had never read any of them. Then one day it happened that one of the books was brought to his attention. He sat down at once to read the lovely descriptions of his city, his palace, and his garden. As he was reading, he came to this statement: "The song of the Nightingale is the loveliest of all."

The Emperor had never heard of the Nightingale until he read that statement. "What Nightingale?" he cried. "How could there be a Nightingale that sings in my garden when I have never heard it?"

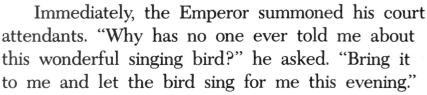

Immediately, the Emperor summoned his court attendants. "Why has no one ever told me about this wonderful singing bird?" he asked. "Bring it to me and let the bird sing for me this evening."

But the court attendants had never seen the bird, and not one of them even knew anything about it. They searched every room in the palace, looking for someone who had heard the Nightingale.

The search was in vain until at last, in the kitchen, they asked a girl who was busily scrubbing pots and pans. "Of course I know the Nightingale!" she exclaimed. "I know it very well."

Gladly, the girl agreed to take the court attendants to the forest. They walked through the lovely flowers in the garden, and just as they entered the tall trees, the Nightingale began to sing. The attendants listened in amazement. Never before had they heard such music.

"Little Nightingale," called the kitchen maid, "our most gracious Emperor would like very much for you to sing for him."

"With the greatest pleasure," answered the Nightingale. "My song sounds best in the forest, but I shall willingly follow you to the palace."

The whole court was present in the great hall of the palace. The Emperor nodded, and the Nightingale began to sing. It sang so sweetly and beautifully that tears came into the Emperor's eyes.

"Stay with us, little Nightingale," the Emperor cried, "and you shall have everything you desire."

"I will stay," said the Nightingale, "but I am rewarded enough. I have seen tears in the Emperor's eyes."

So the Nightingale stayed at the palace. It lived in a splendid cage and was given everything it desired. Then, one day, a package marked "The Nightingale" arrived. When it was opened, it was found to contain a beautifully made mechanical bird, covered with diamonds and precious stones. When it was wound up, the mechanical bird sang one of the songs that the real Nightingale sang.

"Oh, this is splendid!" cried the ladies and gentlemen of the court. The Emperor was also delighted and called for the mechanical bird to sing again and again. No one noticed the real Nightingale as it flew out through an open window and started on its way back to the forest.

Five years passed, and the mechanical bird sang every day. Each time it was wound up, it sang the same song in exactly the same way.

Then suddenly, a great sorrow came to the city. The Emperor became seriously ill, and the court doctors said he was close to death. As they leaned over the dying Emperor, the doctors heard him whisper, "Music! Music! Make the mechanical golden bird sing."

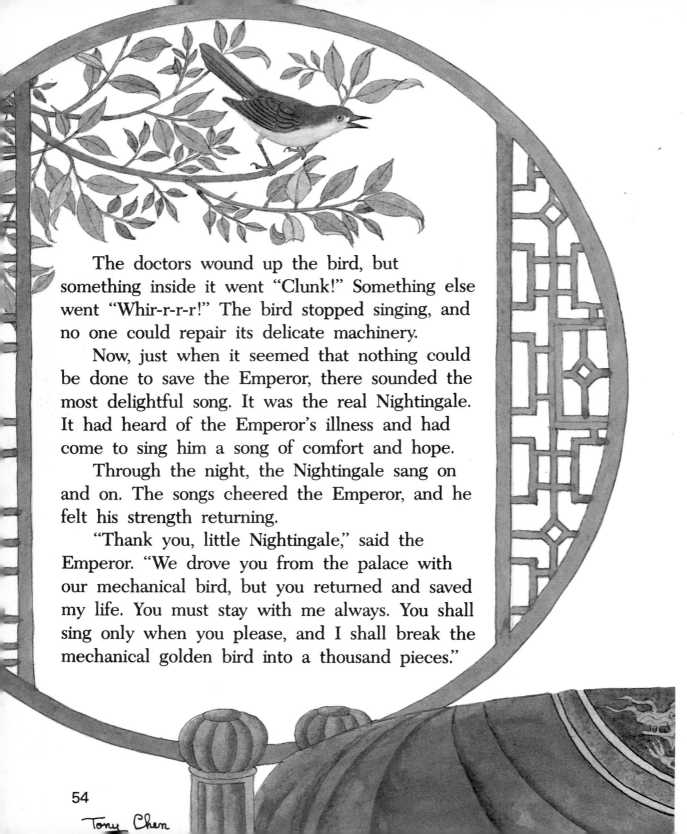

The doctors wound up the bird, but something inside it went "Clunk!" Something else went "Whir-r-r-r!" The bird stopped singing, and no one could repair its delicate machinery.

Now, just when it seemed that nothing could be done to save the Emperor, there sounded the most delightful song. It was the real Nightingale. It had heard of the Emperor's illness and had come to sing him a song of comfort and hope.

Through the night, the Nightingale sang on and on. The songs cheered the Emperor, and he felt his strength returning.

"Thank you, little Nightingale," said the Emperor. "We drove you from the palace with our mechanical bird, but you returned and saved my life. You must stay with me always. You shall sing only when you please, and I shall break the mechanical golden bird into a thousand pieces."

Tony Chen

"No," said the Nightingale. "Don't destroy the mechanical bird. It sang the best it could for as long as it could. As for me, I cannot live in a palace, but I will come to visit you every night. I will sit on a bough outside your window and sing.

With that, the Nightingale flew away, and the Emperor fell into a deep sleep.

The next morning, the sorrowing servants and court attendants came to mourn their Emperor, for they had expected him to die during the night. When they opened the door, however, there stood the Emperor at a window. He turned around and startled them with a strong and cheery "Good morning!"

There followed great rejoicing in the land, for the Emperor was well and strong again. And every evening, he threw open the windows of his room to hear the lovely songs of the Nightingale.

THE TUESDAY ELEPHANT

Nancy Garfield

There once was a boy of ten named Kwani. He lived in a tribe called the Kamba. It was in the country of Kenya on the eastern side of the continent of Africa.

Kwani was one of the youngest boys in his family. There were ten brothers and sisters in all. After school, he was often free to walk about the countryside.

Sometimes he wandered down a hill and sat under the shade of the Mchungwa tree. He peered out at the green field ahead, dreaming. Thinking and dreaming. Watching the sun set in the lazy afternoon.

One day he heard a sound in the bush. He jumped up. Staring straight at him was a baby elephant.

Kwani stood still. He tried not to make a sound. Then the tiny elephant walked up to him and tickled his shoulder with his trunk. Kwani laughed. "Hello, mtoto tembo—hello, little elephant," he said. And then he patted him on the neck.

Suddenly there was a great noise. Kwani saw the mother elephant approaching. She was making all kinds of sounds. He hid at the side of the tree. Then the little elephant ran off to its mother.

From that day on, Kwani often visited that spot. He was hoping to see his friend the baby elephant. And the elephant often came to see Kwani. Kwani named him "Jumanne tembo," or Tuesday Elephant, because that was the day they met.

Over many months Kwani and the Tuesday Elephant became good friends. Kwani often brought berries for the elephant to eat. And sometimes they would get into the shallow part of the river and get wet. Jumanne always sprayed Kwani's back. And they laughed and laughed and laughed.

They could never stay very long in the water. They had to watch out for crocodiles.

Kwani would often go to the forest and play with Jumanne. He would climb on Jumanne's fuzzy-haired back. For baby elephants are covered with soft, black fuzz. They would walk along the banks of the river.

Kwani would run into the forest after school was out. Every day, he would part the bush and whisper, "Jumanne, I am here. Miye, Kwani—it is I, Kwani." And slowly, quietly, Jumanne would come and tap Kwani with his trunk.

They would both run to the path by the river's edge. Often they would see wild geese or ducks drinking. Sometimes the deer and gazelles stood gracefully against the other shore in the sunlight.

Sometimes Kwani took his littlest brother Maliki to meet the elephant. But he made him swear to keep this a secret. And his littlest brother swore. So the secret was kept.

Always Kwani had looked forward to the annual elephant hunt. It was a big event.

The hunters of the tribe tried to catch an elephant. All the children of the village waited to hear of the news that an elephant had been caught.

But this year Kwani did not look forward to the elephant hunt. It was with sadness that he greeted the morning of the hunt. Kwani's eyes were wet with tears. Only his littlest brother knew why he had cried all night. Only his littlest brother knew of his friend Jumanne.

Kwani had tried to warn Jumanne in the weeks before the hunt. "Ficha," he said. "Hide, Jumanne, hide from the wicked hunters—ficha, ficha, ficha."

But Jumanne just ran his trunk along Kwani's back and tickled him. Kwani did not think Jumanne understood him.

The sun came up the day of the hunt. Kwani once more stole out in the early dawn. The forest was filled with a white, spidery morning mist. Some of the leaves shone like wax in the early morning sunlight. Heavy, dark green shadows fell beneath the brush and under the trees.

Kwani was running and running to warn Jumanne. Then he heard the hunters shouting. The hunting scouts had brought back word of a herd down the hill.

The hunters shouted, "Kwani, ondoka rudi, ondoka rudi—go away, go back." And so Kwani did.

He sat on the steps of his hut with his littlest brother. And they cried for the little elephant.

The hunters had set the trap, after digging a deep hole in the elephant path. They laid sharp poison-tipped sticks inside it. And they all waited. It was an ugly day for Kwani.

For to Kwani, the elephant was the gentle king of the forest. He and Maliki played behind the hut. They covered a mound of hay with a white cloth. And they cried for Kwani's beloved elephant.

Kwani wore a red cape made of his mother's kerchief. She wondered why he borrowed it. And she wondered why he and Maliki were weeping so loudly. So did everyone. But no one asked. They knew they would get no answer.

Finally the day was ending. All was quiet. The hunters returned. They were all chattering away.

The herd had disappeared magically. It was as if someone had told them to run. A great smile came across Kwani's face. "Littlest brother," he whispered, "have you heard? They have spared my baby elephant Jumanne."

And Kwani thanked the moon and the stars and all the gods for saving Jumanne.

Often now Kwani returned to the forest. He sat under the Mchungwa tree. There he waited for Jumanne to come back. Kwani waited and waited many, many months. Jumanne did not come back.

Sometimes his littlest brother came and sat with him. They stared together out across the clearing. Kwani carved many, many elephants. And the people of his tribe never understood why he called them Jumanne elephants. Only his littlest brother understood.

Kwani waited many afternoons as the sun set. The sky would darken from its fiery orange until it turned hot pink and then red. Finally it turned dark into a deep, deep blue. And Kwani would wander home as the first star appeared.

Kwani had all but given up hope. Then one day he saw a tall, handsome elephant. He was standing in the clearing.

Kwani looked at him. "Jumanne," he said, "Jumanne." And the elephant approached him. He rubbed his trunk along Kwani's back. And Kwani knew it was his Jumanne.

They laughed for a while. Kwani realized that Jumanne had grown very big and handsome. He was no longer a baby elephant. He had left his herd to travel many miles just to visit Kwani. And then Kwani knew it was time to say good-bye.

"Kwa heri," he whispered. "Kwa heri—good-bye. For I know you must get back to your herd." And Kwani watched Jumanne leave the clearing. He was going off through the bush to find his herd again.

Kwani waved good-bye. Then the sun gave a golden glow to the entire forest. And Kwani turned to go back home.

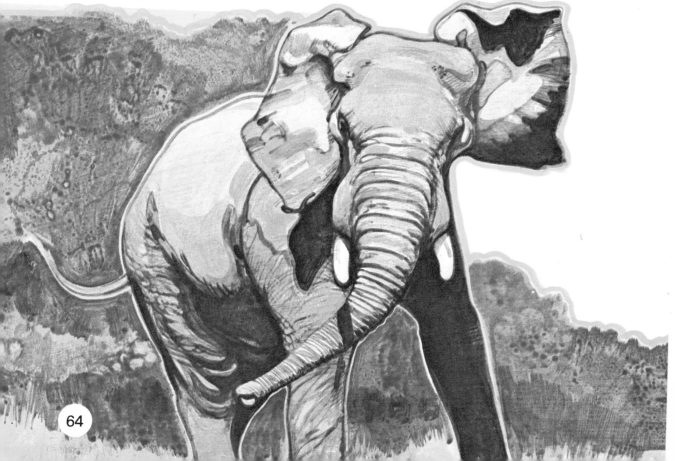

What Does It Mean?

What do you do when you come to a word that you don't know in a sentence? You can use a dictionary to find its pronunciation and meaning. But there is another way to figure out the meaning of an unknown word. You can use other words in the sentence that you do know.

When you are using other words to figure out the meaning of a word, you are using context clues. The words in the sentence that surround your new word are the context clues.

Here is an example of the way you can use context clues to figure out the meanings of unknown words. The unknown words below are from the story "The Tuesday Elephant." They are words in the Swahili language which is spoken in Kenya.

> Kwani laughed. "Hello, mtoto tembo—hello, little elephant," he said.

From the other words in the sentence, you can figure out that *mtoto tembo* means "little elephant." But do you know which Swahili word means "little" and which means "elephant"? The following sentence may give you the clues you need.

> Kwani named him "Jumanne tembo," or Tuesday elephant, because that was the day they met.

If you study the sentences, you can figure out that *tembo* means "elephant," because it is in both Swahili phrases. What word means "little"? What word means "Tuesday"?

There are other Swahili words in "The Tuesday Elephant." Find these words and try to figure out their meanings by using context clues.

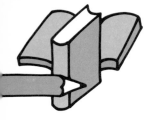

What Is a Paragraph?

A *paragraph* is a group of sentences telling about one subject. The *main-idea sentence* states the most important idea of the paragraph. The *detail sentences* tell about the main idea. Read the following paragraph.

Desert animals stay cool in different ways. Some find shade under rocks. Others stay near trees and bushes. Some desert animals even dig into the cool ground.

The paragraph tells how desert animals stay cool. The first sentence is the main-idea sentence. The other sentences are detail sentences.

ACTIVITY A   Read the detail sentences below. Then read the three main-idea sentences. Decide which main-idea sentence goes with the detail sentences. Write the best main-idea sentence.

Detail sentences:
In early days, everyone traveled by foot. Later, people used boats. Then the car was invented. Today, people fly in jet planes.

Main-idea sentences:
1. Walking is the best way to travel.
2. Travel has changed over the years.
3. Jet planes are faster than cars.

ACTIVITY B   Read the main-idea sentence. Then read the detail sentences. Write the three detail sentences that belong with the main-idea sentence.

Main-idea sentence:
Astronauts walked on the moon in 1969.
Detail sentences:
1. The walk lasted about two hours.
2. The astronauts collected moon rocks.
3. Astronauts can be men or women.
4. They put an American flag on the moon.
5. Some rockets have landed on Mars.

ACTIVITY C   Read the two main-idea sentences. Then read the four detail sentences. Write each main-idea sentence with its detail sentences.

Main-idea sentences:
1. An encyclopedia volume is a book of information.
2. Sets of encyclopedia are found in many places.
Detail sentences:
a. Libraries keep sets of encyclopedia.
b. It tells of famous people.
c. It describes important events.
d. Some people have them at home.

ACTIVITY D   Read the detail sentences. Then write a main-idea sentence for the detail sentences.

Detail sentences:
The sun provides light for us to see. It gives us warmth, too. The sun also helps plants grow.

STATE HOUSE

SAMUEL ADAMS

PHILLIS WHEATLEY

Kathryn Kilby Borland and Helen Ross Speicher

The American colonies began to rebel against British *rule* when the British passed the Stamp Act in 1765. According to this law, the colonists had to pay a small tax on all legal papers.

Groups formed to protest the Stamp Act. One group was called the Sons of Liberty. Soon they forced the British to repeal the law. The colonists were very happy. At this time, Phillis Wheatley was a young slave. She lived in Boston with the Wheatley family. Even under the cruel system of slavery some slave owners were kind to their slaves. The Wheatley's son, Nat, taught Phillis and his sister, Mary, many of the things he was learning in school. When the Stamp Act was repealed, Phillis wanted the British king to know just how happy the American colonists were. So she wrote a poem to King George that had interesting results.

Phillis sat up in bed. It wasn't daylight. Some sound must have awakened her. But now the night was quiet again. She lay back and closed her eyes, wondering whether she was mistaken. Then she heard a bell ringing. It rang again and again, louder and louder.

Phillis ran and opened her window. She leaned out into the May darkness. Far down the street, she could hear a horse's hoofbeats. Then a man on horseback came riding down the street. He was shouting. But Phillis could not understand what he said.

Now she could hear Mr. Wheatley's window being thrown up with an angry sound. "What's all this?" he called out.

"Good news! Good news!" the horseman shouted. But he didn't slow down.

Phillis noticed lighted windows in other houses up and down the street. One or two men had come out on the front steps. They were wearing dressing gowns over their nightshirts.

"What is it?" they called to one another. Nobody seemed to know.

Before long, a group of young men came running down the street with lighted torches. They were throwing their hats in the air.

"Three cheers for King George! Three cheers for the Sons of Liberty!" they shouted. Finally, Mr. Wheatley got the attention of one of the young men.

"We have good news about the Stamp Act, sir," the man called. "Word just came. The Stamp Act has been repealed!"

Phillis could hear Nat's shout from his room. "We did it! We did it!"

No one in the Wheatley house, or probably in all of Boston, went back to sleep that night. The bells went on ringing. Soon drums were beating steadily. And once in a while the boom of a cannon could be heard.

The celebration lasted all day. Bands wandered through the crowds, playing loudly if not well. The bells kept ringing.

That night, there was a fireworks display on the Commons. There had never been such fireworks in Boston. The air was filled with rockets, bright serpents, and spinning pinwheels. At eleven o'clock, twenty-one rockets and sixteen dozen serpents were sent up all at once for a glorious finish.

A loud cheer went up for King George. Phillis wished that King George could know how happy the people were about what had been done. She wished someone would tell him.

After Phillis went to bed that night, she tossed and turned. Some idea was trying to form in her brain. But she was too tired to think about it.

In the middle of the night, the idea suddenly came to her.

She would write King George about how the colonists felt. Perhaps she could even write it in verse. She had written a poem not long before, but had not shown it to anyone.

She crept quietly out of bed. Her candle burned for hours while she wrote. When she woke up in the morning, she looked at what she had written.

"What a silly idea," she thought. "How could I ever have imagined that the king would read anything written by a young slave?" She left the poem on the little table by her bed and almost forgot it.

A few weeks later, Phillis was sick in bed with a cold. One morning, Mrs. Wheatley brought a bowl of porridge for her breakfast. As she set the bowl on the little table, she noticed a scrap of paper there. She picked up the paper and asked, "What is this, Phillis?"

Phillis was embarrassed. "Oh, it's nothing, Mrs. Wheatley, nothing at all."

"But it is, Phillis. These are beautiful words. Did you copy this poem from a book?"

"Oh, no, Mrs. Wheatley. I wrote it myself, but it really isn't very good."

"You wrote it yourself? Phillis, this is remarkable. Why didn't you show it to us?"

"I was ashamed to show it to you, Mrs. Wheatley. I actually wrote it to send to the king. And then I decided that would be silly. Besides, the poem isn't any good."

"May I show it to Mr. Wheatley?"

Phillis hesitated. Probably Mr. Wheatley would think the poem was foolish. But she said, "Yes, of course." Mrs. Wheatley did not seem to notice her lack of enthusiasm.

That evening after supper, the whole family came up to her room. Mr. Wheatley was holding the poem in his hand. He looked very solemn. Phillis feared he was angry. Then he cleared his throat and said, "Mrs. Wheatley tells me you wrote this poem."

"Yes, sir," Phillis answered.

"Now are you sure you really wrote it yourself? Sometimes we read something and don't remember it. Later we remember it but don't remember where we saw it. Then we may think we thought of it ourselves. Do you see what I mean, Phillis?"

"Yes, sir, I do," Phillis said, "But that isn't the way it was this time. I wanted somehow to make King George see how grateful we were. This was the only way I could think of. I know it was foolish of me, sir. I guess I was just excited over the celebration."

"I told you, Father," Mary said. "Phillis reads and reads and reads. She uses words I don't even know how to use."

Mr. Wheatley cleared his throat again. "Well, then," he said, "in that case, it's remarkable. Have you written any other poems?"

"Yes, sir. I wrote one about Harvard College. Would you like to see it?"

A few minutes later, Mr. Wheatley left the room with both poems in his hand. Then one evening several days later, he told Phillis that she was to go to the State House with him the next morning. "A few gentlemen there would like to ask you about your poems."

"They'll be angry," Phillis thought. "Mr. Wheatley shouldn't have told them."

Usually Phillis enjoyed looking at the lion over the State House door. Today, she had too many things on her mind even to think about it. Mr. Wheatley had told her that the most important men in Boston would talk with her.

Mr. Wheatley led her into the Council Chamber. Several stern-looking men who were seated at a long table looked up at her. Others looked down from gold frames on the wall.

"Stand at this end of the table where we can see you," one of the men said. He was holding her poems in his hand.

"Yes, sir," Phillis said in a low voice. She folded her hands in front of her. That stopped them from shaking.

"Mr. Wheatley tells us you wrote these poems," said one of the men.

"Yes, sir."

"Did anyone give you any help?"

"No, sir."

"Why did you write about Harvard College?"

"Because, sir, Mr. Nat brought back so much from there for Miss Mary and me to study and talk about. He even taught Latin to Miss Mary. And she taught it to me."

"Latin, eh?" a man said with interest. "Can you tell me what *E pluribus unum* means?"

Phillis smiled. "Yes, sir. It means 'one from many,'" she said.

Some of the other gentlemen asked questions in Latin which she was able to answer. They also asked her what books she liked to read. Then they began asking about her poems.

"Tell us what you meant by these lines, 'May every clime with equal gladness see/A monarch's smile can set his subjects free.'"

The speaker was Mr. Samuel Adams. Phillis had often seen him at the Wheatley's house. "I meant that we were glad the king used his power to make us happy. I'm sorry the meaning wasn't clear, sir," she said.

"I think it was quite clear."

The other gentlemen nodded. They asked her questions almost all morning. She was so tired before they were through that she hardly knew what she answered.

At the end of the questioning, Mr. Adams smiled and said, "We shall send your poem to the king. And we hope that you will write many more. You have a great gift, young woman, a very great gift, and it must be used."

THE SHOESHINE CHAIR

Janice May Udry

One of Angie's favorite places was the secondhand store. The sign in front said "Antiques and Junk for Sale." The old store had three rooms. The front room contained expensive furniture and dishes. But items in the second room cost less. In the third room was the junk. Some things in the junk room cost less than a dollar. The junk room overflowed out into a weedy fenced-in junkyard in the back.

Angie went to the secondhand store. She hoped to find an unusual but inexpensive present for her father's birthday.

"Have you got any really good junk today, Mr. Whitaker?" asked Angie.

"Sure I have, Angie. Just look around. There's a little bit of everything out there in back," said Mr. Whitaker from behind his messy, dusty old desk.

Mr. Whitaker told Angie he had been collecting stuff since he was six years old. Angie looked around his store.

"That's not hard to believe," she said.

"If you think I've got a lot here," he chuckled, "you ought to see my house."

Angie poked around the store for a long time. But she didn't see anything that seemed just right for her father's birthday. Before she left, she decided to take one last turn around the junkyard.

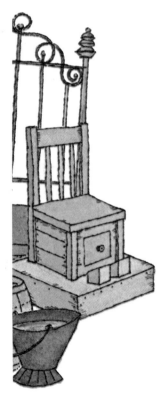

There, lying on its side, she found something that really interested her. It was an old, homemade wooden shoeshine chair. A thin straight chair had been nailed to a large box with a drawer in it. The drawer pulled open with a spool. The chair and the box were nailed to a platform with two wooden footrests on it. The whole thing had been painted sky-blue. It was all loose and rickety now.

"But some nails will fix it up fine," thought Angie.

"How much for the shoeshine chair?" Angie asked Mr. Whitaker.

"You found one of my best pieces of junk," said Mr. Whitaker. "How much money have you got?"

"Fifty cents," said Angie.

"It's a deal," said Mr. Whitaker. "The shoe-shine chair is yours. I'll tell Joe to deliver it to your house when he's taking that sofa over to the Bensons'."

That afternoon Mrs. Brinker answered the doorbell.

"Where do you want this, ma'am?"

"What is it?" asked Mrs. Brinker.

"It's your shoeshine chair, ma'am," said Joe.

"I think you have the wrong address. Wait a minute. Angie!"

Angie came to the hall. "That's mine, Mother. Just leave it on the porch, please."

Joe put the chair down and went back to his truck.

"Angie! Is that what you got your father for his birthday?" asked Mrs. Brinker.

"No," said Angie, "I didn't find anything yet. I bought this for myself. I know it looks

rickety right now, but I'll work on it. All it
needs are some new nails, here and there."

"It makes our front porch look really different," said Mrs. Brinker.

"It has a lot of possibilities," said Angie.

Angie was very pleased when she had
made the old chair sturdy again with nails. It
made a wonderful throne.

When her friend Molly came over with her
skates, Angie had an idea.

"Hey, Molly, let's put this throne on wheels."

In a little while, Angie and Molly were
pushing each other up and down the street in
a strange-looking, high wheelchair. They had
nailed their skates to the bottom of the shoeshine chair.

"That was one of my best ideas," said
Angie later, when they sat resting on the front
steps. "But I still haven't bought a present for
my father. His birthday is day after tomorrow.

I spent all the money I had on the shoeshine
chair. I know what I'd like to buy him."

"What?" asked Molly.

"Have you ever been in the new gourmet
shop?" asked Angie. "Do you know that they
have jars of fried grasshoppers there? That's
what I'd like to buy. He's never had that. And
he'd never guess what it was. Wouldn't it be
fun to taste a fried grasshopper?"

"Oh, Angie!" Molly made a face.

"But I haven't got two dollars," said Angie.
For awhile she was deep in thought.

"Come on, Angie. Let's take turns riding
in the chair again," said Molly.

"O.K.," said Angie, getting up.

The young twins who lived down the block
ran out when they saw Angie pushing Molly
past their house.

"Angie! Angie! Where did you get that?
Can we have a ride?" they begged.

After Angie and Molly had given each of the twins a ride, they didn't want to get out of the chair.

"Please give us another ride! It's fun."

"No more today," said Angie.

"*Please!*"

Angie's face suddenly brightened. "No more *free* rides. Have you got any money?"

The twins nodded.

"Well," said Angie, "for five cents I'll give you a ride all the way around the block."

"O.K.!" The twins dashed away. "Stay there. We'll be right back!"

Angie grinned at Molly. "Do you know what we're going to do?"

"What?"

"Earn the money for my father's present," said Angie.

"How much money do you think the twins have got?" asked Molly.

"Not just them. We'll give anybody who wants one a ride for five cents," said Angie. "Wait here with the chair. I'll be right back."

Angie ran home. She came back with a small can of paint and a brush. On both sides of the box under the chair she wrote:

"Ride—5¢."

As they pushed the twins around the block, other children appeared. Like magic they ran into their houses and popped out again with nickels in their hands. Some of them rode more than once.

By dinnertime, Angie and Molly were very tired, since some of their riders had demanded fast rides.

"We have to go home now," they told some of the waiting customers. "But we'll be out tomorrow."

Angie and Molly pushed the chair home and into Angie's garage. They counted almost a dollar.

"We'll make another dollar easy," said Angie. "See you tomorrow, Molly. Go to bed early so you won't be tired tomorrow."

"I feel like going to bed right now," said Molly.

Angie grinned. "Remember you're invited to my father's birthday dinner. And you'll get to taste fried grasshoppers, Molly!"

The next morning, Angie and Molly added a parasol and a bell to the chair ride. Many of the small children liked the ride even better now. They could sit up high under the parasol ringing a bell, while being pushed along the sidewalk.

By the middle of the afternoon, they had plenty of money for the present.

Angie's mother drove the girls down to the gourmet shop.

"I always like to go in here," said Angie. "People look as if they are enjoying themselves, and they aren't in any hurry. The ice cream store is like that, too. People in ice cream stores and gourmet shops are usually in a good mood."

Angie led Molly into the store and down one aisle.

"Here it is," said Angie. "See, you get quite a large can of grasshoppers for two dollars."

"I wonder what my father would say if I gave him fried grasshoppers for his birthday," giggled Molly.

"It's a nice change from neckties," said Angie.

"This feels like a new can of pipe tobacco," said Mr. Brinker that night, after they had all had a piece of cake.

He untied the ribbon and took off the paper. "Grasshoppers! *Fried* grasshoppers," cried Mr. Brinker with delight. "I have always wanted to taste them." He selected a grasshopper and passed the can. "Help yourselves," he said. "This is a very special treat."

There was a moment of silence. They held their grasshoppers between thumb and forefinger.

They all waited for someone to take the first bite.

"Don't they look yummy?" said Mrs. Brinker.

"Oh, they certainly do," said Mr. Brinker, looking at his grasshopper.

Molly giggled nervously.

"O.K., everybody, one, two, three," said Angie. She popped her grasshopper into her mouth. So did Mr. and Mrs. Brinker. And after taking a deep breath, so did Molly.

They munched in silence, watching each other's faces.

"They are very crunchy," said Mr. Brinker. He ate another one.

"I believe I prefer potato chips," said Mrs. Brinker.

"We're just not used to the idea of eating grasshoppers," said Angie. "In some countries, it's just a plain, ordinary everyday thing to eat grasshoppers."

"My brother will never believe me when I tell him that I ate a grasshopper," said Molly. "May I take one to him?"

"Help yourself," said Mr. Brinker.

"Take several," said Mrs. Brinker. "There's plenty."

"Thank you for such an unusual present, Angie," said Mr. Brinker.

"You're welcome," grinned Angie.

Read and think about these words from the story "The Shoeshine Chair": *shoeshine, doorbell, snowman, birthday.* Can you tell how these words are alike? If you can, then you know that words like these are called *compound words.* Compound words are two words that go together to form a new word with a meaning all its own.

shoe + shine = shoeshine

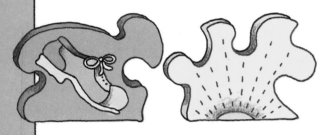

Sometimes you can figure out the meaning of the compound word by thinking about the meaning of each separate word and seeing how the two words fit together.

Look at the word *shoeshine.* You know what a shoe is. Think about what the word *shine* means. These two meanings fit together in this way:

A shoeshine is a shine
for a shoe.

Use this same idea to find the meaning of the word *doorbell.*

A doorbell is a ____ for a ____.

Meanings of other compound words can be figured out in another way. Look at the word *snowman.* Think about what snow is. You know the meaning of *man.* These meanings fit together in this way:

A man of snow is a snowman.

Use this same idea to find the meaning of the word *birthday.*

The ____ of your ____
is your birthday.

Now look at the compound words below. Can you find the meaning of each compound word?

mailbox   junkyard
raindrops handshake

A NEW SONG

Laura Adams Armer

Younger Brother and Uncle had finally rounded up all the horses. The Big Man from the trading post was expected in a few days. He would look them over and choose what he wanted. The next task was to find the steers. The little Navaho boy had been excused from herding the sheep so that he could help Uncle. They were riding their ponies up a narrow gorge. They were keeping a sharp lookout for the red-and-white yearling that was missing. Tracks led to the water hole. There in the damp sand beside the water they found new tracks. They were the tracks of the mountain lion.

"The Soft-footed Chief has been hunting," Uncle said. "He is a good hunter and grows fat on our cattle."

Younger Brother hoped his yearling had not helped to fatten the Soft-footed Chief. Uncle had given the yearling to him when it was just a little calf. He had watched it grow and was very proud of it. He asked Uncle if they would hunt the mountain lion.

"No, my child. He is one of the pets the Turquoise Woman gave to our people. It is better that we leave him to follow his own trail of beauty."

"Uncle, where does the Turquoise Woman live?"

"On an island in the wide water of the west. There she lives in her turquoise house with her husband. He carries the sun."

"And when the Sun Bearer reaches his home in the west, what does he do with the sun, Uncle?"

"He hangs it up on the turquoise peg on the turquoise wall of the turquoise house of the Turquoise Woman. It goes *tla, tla, tla, tla,* as it sways on the wall. When the sun is still, the Sun Bearer lights his pipe from its fire. But he cannot rest too long. Every morning he must start across the sky from the east, bearing the sun on his left shoulder."

"I should like to go to the wide water of the west, Uncle. I should like to see the turquoise house and the Turquoise Woman."

The two talked as they rode.

They were following a narrow stream of water that traced its way under the tall, tender green trees. The trail their ponies followed was narrow and overgrown. Sometimes Younger Brother wondered if it were a trail, it was so full of loose rocks.

He was glad Uncle had let him ride with him. Uncle was a medicine man who knew the stories of the Holy People. The Holy People had lived in the land before the Navahos came. They were the people who built their homes in caves high up in the cliffs. They must have been a busy people. Many broken bits of their pottery could be found lying about the country. The designs on the old pots were painted in black on white or red backgrounds. The designs were strange to the Navahos. Sometimes the Navaho people copied the designs in their weavings.

Uncle had told Younger Brother many stories of the ancient people. He had told him about the boy who wanted to find a new song. And he had told

Younger Brother how the boy had traveled on a rainbow to reach the House of Dawn. Younger Brother had seen the House of Dawn and the House of Evening Twilight, high in a canyon wall. They were so high that everyone knew they could be reached only by a rainbow trail.

Younger Brother wondered if there were any stone houses of the ancient ones near where they were riding. Uncle said he had never before been so far up the canyon wall. Maybe no one had. It was very wild. The trail had given out. They were forced to ride uphill through brush and over loose rocks. They were still looking for the lost yearling.

Breaking through the brush, they came into a clear space. There, at the foot of a cliff, they found a spring of water. It fed the stream they had been following. Younger Brother could hardly believe his eyes when he saw his own red-and-white yearling drinking at the spring.

"Uncle," he whispered, "the Soft-footed Chief did not kill my yearling."

"It is well, my child. I will rope him and we will lead him home."

While Uncle roped the yearling, Younger Brother rode around the end of the cliff. He liked this country with its rocks and mountains and trees. He felt happy. He thought again about the story of the boy who wanted to find a new song. He thought that he, too, would like to make a new song.

Suddenly, the stillness of the mountains was broken by a queer sound like the rattling of hoofs on stone. Younger Brother looked in the direction of the sound. He saw a huge round cave in the mountainside. It was filled with many little stone houses. A blue shadow partly hid them.

Younger Brother could still hear the clattering, rattling noise. Then, into a streak of sunshine on the floor of the cave, leaped seven slender deer. Just for a moment they paused in the light. Then they leaped and danced on the stone floor and were lost to sight in the bushes in front of the cave.

Everything was again still except Younger Brother's heart.

97

That was beating wildly and words were pounding in his head to be let out. He knew he had found a new song and the words poured out of him like the song of the bluebirds. This is what he sang:

> *In the yellow sun they danced,*
> *Slender Horns and Slender*
>   *Feet.*
> *Near their shadowed homes*
>   *they danced.*
> *Slender Horns and Slender*
>   *Feet.*

Then he rode back to Uncle and whispered, "The Deer People! I saw them enter their houses."

Uncle looked at the child. His big brown eyes were opened wide. He was breathing fast and trembling. Uncle knew something had happened. Probably the boy had been blessed with a vision. That was good. He would make a powerful medicine man if he had visions. He spoke to him.

"It is well, my child. We will

return home. Tonight you may tell us all about the Deer People."

Riding back and leading the red-and-white yearling, Younger Brother was very quiet. He knew he had seen the homes of the ancients. That night in the hogan by the fire he sang his new song for Uncle.

Uncle was pleased. "It is a new song. Never have I heard it before," he said. "Now you must have a new name. I shall call you Little Singer. Because the Deer People danced for you, I shall teach you their songs. It will take many years to learn them. Not until you are a man will you know them all, but we shall begin in four days."

Nobody believed that Younger Brother had seen a real cave with real houses. Only the Big Man believed because he knew that anything magic or wonderful could exist and did exist in Navaho land. Besides, he had a photograph of the big cave with all the houses. He had never shown it to anyone because he too liked to watch the Deer People dance in the sunlight. He knew they never would if noisy people went to their homes with guns and canned goods. So he and Younger Brother kept the secret together.

No One Else

Now, someone else can tell you how
To multiply by three
And someone else can tell you how
To spell Schenectady
And someone else can tell you how
To ride a two-wheeled bike
But no one else, no, no one else
Can tell you what to like.

An engineer can tell you how
To run a railroad train
A map can tell you where to find
The capital of Spain
A book can tell you all the names
Of every star above
But no one else, no, no one else
Can tell you who to love.

Your aunt Louise can tell you how
To plant a pumpkin seed
Your cousin Frank can tell you how
To catch a centipede
Your Mom and Dad can tell you how
To brush between each meal
But no one else, no, no one else
Can tell you how to feel.

For how you feel is how you feel
And all the whole world through
No one else, no, no one else
Knows that as well as YOU!

—*Elaine Laron*

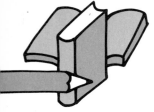

Forms of Literature

Imagine that you have just finished your homework. You turn on the TV. You see a news reporter. She says:

> "It's five o'clock. The temperature is forty-five degrees. The wind is five miles an hour. Rain is expected later tonight . . . The President greeted the Prime Minister of India on the White House lawn this afternoon. Stay tuned to Channel 37 for all the latest news."

Now you switch to another channel. There you see three colorful dragons. They are plotting the take-over of a castle in the clouds. You hear:

> "Let's dry up the moat with a wave of the magic wand. Then we'll catch the king in a dragon's dragnet!"
> "Stay tuned to Channel 80 for more adventures of the dangerous dragons."

Which program do you think is about real people and real events? Which is about imaginary people, animals, and events? Stories about real people and real events are called *nonfiction*. Stories about imaginary people, animals, and events are called *fiction*. The news program on the first channel was nonfiction. The dragon story on the second channel was fiction.

Books may be described as fiction or nonfiction, too. Some examples of fiction are books that have fairy tales, legends, myths, and mysteries. Some examples of nonfiction are biographies, histories, science books, and "Do-It-Yourself" books.

Let's see how well you know the difference between fiction and nonfiction. Make two columns on your paper. Label one column, <u>Fiction</u>. Label the other column, <u>Nonfiction</u>. Write your answers to the questions below in the correct column.

1. These selections might be found in a book or a magazine. Which are nonfiction? Which are fiction?
   a. a report on storms
   b. a scary ghost story
   c. a fable about a horse that talks
   d. a short history of Australia

2. These selections may be found in this book. Which are fiction? Which are nonfiction?
   a. "The Medal"
   b. "A New Song"
   c. "Growing Up Chinese-American"
   d. "The Emperor's Nightingale"

3. These books might be found in a library. Which would be fiction? Which would be nonfiction?
   a. *Fish of the Pacific Ocean*
   b. *Aesop's Fables*
   c. *The Chicken Who Visited the Queen*
   d. *George Washington: The First President*

GROWING

The selections you read in "Growing" were about real people and make-believe characters from many different times and places. Some of the people and characters learned how to be brave. Some learned how to develop their talents. Some learned to understand other people's feelings. But they all had one thing in common. They were learning about themselves and others. That's what growing is all about!

Thinking About "Growing"

1. What did Sarah Ida learn about friendship after almost losing Al as a friend?
2. How did Trina and Maggie each have to change and grow in order to keep being friends?
3. Why did Kwani know it was time to say "good-by" to Jumanne?
4. What did Phillis Wheatley and Younger Brother show about themselves when their special talents were discovered?
5. After reading "Growing Up Chinese-American," why do you think that learning about the customs of others helps you to understand other people?
6. Some people think growing means getting older. What do you think it means?

Glossary

This glossary will help you to pronounce and to understand the meanings of some of the unusual or difficult words in this book.

The pronunciation of each word is printed beside the word in this way: **o·pen** (ō′pən). The letters, signs, and key words in the list below will help you read the pronunciation respelling. When an entry word has more than one syllable, a dark accent mark (′) is placed after the syllable that has the heaviest stress. In some words, a light accent mark (′) is placed after the syllable that receives a less heavy stress.

The pronunciation key, syllable breaks, accent mark placements, and phonetic respellings in this glossary are adapted from the Macmillan *Beginning Dictionary* (1977) and the Macmillan *School Dictionary* (1977). Other dictionaries may use other pronunciation symbols.

Pronunciation Key

a bad	**i** it	**oo** wood	**u** cup	**ə** *stands for*
ā cake	**ī** ice	**ōō** food	**ur** turn	a *as in* age
ä father	**j** joke	**oi** oil	**yōō** music	e *as in* taken
b bat	**k** kit	**ou** out	**v** very	i *as in* pencil
ch chin	**l** lid	**p** pail	**w** wet	o *as in* lemon
d dog	**m** man	**r** ride	**y** yes	u *as in* helpful
e pet	**n** not	**s** sit	**z** zoo	
ē me	**ng** sing	**sh** ship	**zh** treasure	
f five	**o** hot	**t** tall		
g game	**ō** open	**th** thin		
h hit	**ô** off	**th** that		

A

aisle (īl) *n.* the space between two rows or sections of something.

a·maze·ment (ə māz'mənt) *n.* overwhelming wonder or surprise; astonishment.

an·cient (ān'shənt) *adj.* having to do with times very long ago; very old.

an·nu·al (an'yoō əl) *adj.* happening or returning once a year; yearly.

an·tique (an tēk') *n.* something made very long ago that is valued for its age, especially something that is more than one hundred years old.

ar·gu·ment (är'gyə mənt) *n.* a discussion of something by people who do not agree.

at·ten·dant (ə ten'dənt) *n.* a person who takes care of or waits on another.

B

ba·king pow·der (bā'king pou'dər) *n.* a powder used in baking to make dough or batter rise.

bead·y (bē'dē) *adj.* small, round, and glittering.

bear·hound (bār'hound') *n.* a dog trained to hunt and chase bears.

bird's nest soup (burdz' nest soōp') *n.* a Chinese soup made from edible bird nests or substitutes.

bough (bou) *n.* a branch of a tree, especially a large or main branch.

C

calf (kaf) *n.* the young of such animals as cows, elephants, whales, and seals.

can·yon (kan'yən) *n.* a deep valley with steep sides, usually with a stream running through it.

cel·e·bra·tion (sel'ə brā'shən) *n.* the ceremonies or festivities carried on to celebrate something.

cen·ti·pede (sen'tə pēd') *n.* any of a group of small animals that resemble worms.

Chi·ca·go (shə ko'gō) *n.* a city in Illinois.

Chi·na·town (chī'nə toun') *n.* a Chinese section of any city outside China, as in San Francisco or New York City.

chop·sticks (chop'stiks') *n.* a pair of long, slender sticks, usually wood or ivory, that are used for eating.

claw (klô) *n.* a nail on the foot of a bird or other animal.

clear·ing (klēr'ing) *n.* a piece of land, especially within a thickly wooded area, that is free of trees and brush.

clime (klīm) *n.* an old-fashioned word for country, region, or climate.

col·o·nist (kol'ə nist) *n.* a person born or living in a colony.

col·o·ny (kol' ə nē) *n. pl.,* **colonies.** a territory that is under the control of another, usually distant, country.

com·mons (kom'ənz) *n.* a plot of land, such as a pasture or park, that is owned or used by the public.

com·pli·ment (kom'plə mənt) *n.* an expression of admiration, flattery, or praise.

con·ti·nent (kont'ən ənt) *n.* one of the seven great land areas of the earth. The continents are Asia, Africa, North America, South America, Antarctica, Europe, and Australia.

crin·kle (kring'kəl) *v.* to form wrinkles or ripples; wrinkle.

croc·o·dile (krok′ ə dīl′) *n.* a large lizard-like animal that has thick skin, a long, narrow snout, strong jaws, and long rows of teeth.

D

del·i·cate (del′i kit) *adj.* fine or dainty in structure, quality, texture, or form.

de·light·ful (di līt′ fəl) *adj.* highly pleasing; giving delight.

Der Chung (dār chung)

Der Wai Lee (dār wā lē)

de·scrip·tion (di skrip′shən) *n.* **1.** a picture in words. **2.** a statement or account that describes.

de·stroy (di stroi′) *v.* to ruin completely; wreck.

dia·mond (dī′mənd, dī′ə mənd) *n.* a mineral that is usually colorless, used as a jewel; the hardest natural substance known.

diamond

dress·ing gown (dres′ing goun′) *n.* a robe, especially a long, loose one, usually worn before or while dressing or for resting.

E

egg roll (eg′ rōl′) *n.* an egg-dough casing filled with minced vegetables and fried.

em·bar·rass·ment (em bar′əs mənt) *n.* the feeling of being uncomfortable or ashamed.

em·per·or (em′pər ər) *n.* the male ruler of an empire.

en·thu·si·asm (en thoo′ zē az′əm) *n.* a strong feeling of excitement and interest about something.

e plu·ri·bus u·num (ē′ ploor′ ə bəs yoo′nəm) out of many, one. It is a Latin phrase and the motto on the official seal of the U.S.

ex·ist (eg zist′) *v.* **1.** to be real; have reality. **2.** to be present or found; occur.

ex·pe·ri·ence (eks pēr′ē əns) *n.* knowledge, skill, or wisdom gained over a period of time.

F

fier·y (fīr′ē) *adj.* like fire; flashing.

foot·rest (foot′rest′) *n.* something, such as a small stool or platform, on which the feet may be rested.

fore·paw (fôr′pô′) *n.* an animal's front paw.

fu·ry (fyoor′ē) *n.* violent, uncontrollable anger.

fuzz (fuz) *n.* fine, loose particles, hair or fibers.

G

gash (gash) *n. pl.,* **gashes.** a long, deep cut or wound.

ga·zelle (gə zel′) *n.* a small, graceful antelope that has a fawn-colored coat with black and white markings, curving horns, and large eyes.

gin·ger (jin′jər) *n.* a spice that is ground from the roots of a tropical plant, used in cooking and medicine.

---

a **b**a**d**, ā **c**a**k**e, ä **f**a**th**e**r**; e **p**e**t**, ē **m**e; i **i**t, i **ī**ce; o **h**o**t**, ō **op**e**n**, ô **o**ff; oo **w**oo**d**; oo **f**oo**d**; oi **oi**l, ou **ou**t; th **th**i**n**, th **th**a**t**; u **c**u**p**, ur **t**ur**n**, yoo **m**u**s**i**c**; zh **tr**ea**s**ure; ə **a**g**o**, tak**e**n, penc**i**l, lem**o**n, helpf**u**l

glass count·er (glas′koun′tər) *n.* a long table, as in a store or restaurant, with a top and sides made of glass. Items for sale are often displayed in glass counters.

glo·ri·ous (glôr′ē əs) *adj.* magnificent; splendid.

gorge (gôrj) *n.* a deep, narrow valley between steep, rocky sides of a mountain.

gour·met (goor mā′) *n.* a person who is an expert in choosing and judging fine food and drink.

grace·ful·ly (grās′fəl ē) *adv.* in a graceful or harmonious manner.

gra·cious (grā′shəs) *adj.* having or showing kindness and courtesy.

H

her·it·age (her′ ə tij) *n.* something that is handed down from previous generations or from the past; tradition.

hes·i·tate (hez′ ə tāt) *v.* to wait or stop for a moment; to pause briefly.

ho·gan (hō′gon) *n.* a dwelling used by the Navaho, usually made of logs and branches covered with earth.

hoof·beat (hoof′bēt′, hoof′bēt′) *n.* the sound made by a hoofed animal when it walks, trots, or runs.

hos·pi·tal (hos′pit əl) *n.* a place where doctors and nurses take care of people who are sick or hurt.

I

in·ex·pen·sive (in′iks pen′siv) *adj.* not costing much; cheap.

in·ter·view (in′tər vyoo′) *n.* a meeting for a specific purpose.

J

jas·mine (jaz′ min) *n.* a fragrant bell-shaped flower growing in yellow, white, or pink clusters.

jig (jig) *n.* a fast lively dance.

Ju·manne (joo mān′)

junk·yard (jungk′ yärd′) *n.* a place where junk is collected, stored, or sold.

jasmine

K

Kam·ba (Kom′bə)

Ken·ya (Kēn′ yə) *n.* a country in Africa.

ker·chief (kur′chif) *n.* a piece of cloth worn over the head or around the neck.

Kwa·ni (kwo′nē)

L

Lat·in (lat′in) *n.* the language of the ancient Romans.

ledge (lej) *n.* a narrow, flat surface jutting out from the side of a mountain or other natural formation.

lin·en (lin′ ən) *n.* a strong cloth woven from flax fibers.

look·out (look′out′) *n.* a sharp watch for something to happen.

M

mag·nif·i·cent (mag nif′ ə sənt) *adj.* splendid; exceptional; outstanding.

Ma·li·ki (mo lē′kē)

Mchung·wa (chung′wə)

me·chan·i·cal (mi kan′i kəl) *adj.* produced or operated by a machine.

med·al (med' əl) *n.* a flat piece of metal bearing a design or inscription.

med·i·cine man (med'ə sin man) *n.* Indian tribesman thought to have magical powers.

mon·arch (mon' ərk) *n.* a person, such as a king or queen, who rules a country.

mound (mound) *n.* **1.** a heap or pile of earth, stone, garbage, and so on. **2.** a small hill.

mount·ain li·on (mount' ən lī' ən) *n.* a large wildcat found mainly in North America, also known as a cougar or a puma.

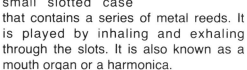

mountain lion

mouth harp (mouth härp) *n.* a musical wind instrument consisting of a small slotted case that contains a series of metal reeds. It is played by inhaling and exhaling through the slots. It is also known as a mouth organ or a harmonica.

mus·tard greens (mus'tərd grēnz) *n., pl.* the edible green leaves of any of several plants, such as broccoli, cabbage, and turnips, belonging to the mustard family.

N

nar·cis·sus (när sis'əs) *n.* a showy yellow or white flower.

Nav·a·ho (nav' ə hō) *n.* a member of a tribe of North American Indians living in New Mexico, Arizona, and Utah.

night·in·gale (nīt' ən gāl', nī' ting gāl') *n.* a small bird with reddish-brown feathers and a whitish breast.

night·shirt (nīt' shurt') *n.* a long shirt worn for sleeping.

nightingale

O

o·pin·ion (ə pin'yən) *n.* a belief or conclusion based on a person's judgment rather than on what is proven or known to be true.

o·pos·sum (ə pos' əm) *n.* a small furry animal that lives in trees and carries its young in a pouch.

o·ver·grown (ō vər grōn') *adj.* covered with weeds, vines, or other growth.

opposum

P

par·a·sol (par' ə sol') *n.* a small, lightweight umbrella usually used as a protection from the sun.

pa·tient (pa' shənt) *adj.* being able to put up with hardship, pain, trouble, or delay without getting angry or upset.

peer (pēr) *v.* to look closely or searchingly.

---

a b**a**d, ā c**a**ke, ä f**a**ther; e p**e**t, ē m**e**; i **i**t, ī **i**ce; o h**o**t, ō **o**pen, ô **o**ff; oo w**oo**d, o͞o f**oo**d; oi **oi**l, ou **ou**t; th **th**in, th **th**at; u c**u**p, ur t**u**rn, yo͞o m**u**sic; zh trea**s**ure; ə **a**go, tak**e**n, penc**i**l, lem**o**n, helpf**u**l

peg (peg) *n.* a piece of wood, metal, or other hard substance that can be fitted or driven into a surface to fasten parts together or to serve as a marker.

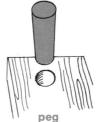

peg

poi·son-tipped (poi′ zən tipt′) *adj.* having the tip covered with a drug or other substance that causes sickness or death.

por·ce·lain (pôr′ sə lin) *n.* a fine ceramic material that is hard and white.

por·ridge (pôr′ ij, por′ ij) *n.* a soft food made by cooking oatmeal or other cereals in water or milk.

pos·si·bil·i·ty (pos′ ə bil′ ə tē) *n. pl.,* **pos·si·bil·i·ties.** something that is possible.

pre·cious (presh′ əs) *adj.* of great cost or value.

pro·test (prə test′) *v.* to object or disapprove of.

R

reb·el (ri bel′) *v.* to refuse to obey laws or authority.

rel·a·tive (rel′ ə tiv) *n.* a person connected with another by blood or marriage.

re·peal (ri pēl′) *v.* to take back; to cancel; do away with something.

res·o·lu·tion (rez′ ə lōō′ shən) *n.* something decided upon; vow.

re·spect (ri spekt′) *v.* to have or show consideration or respect.

re·sult (ri zult′) *n.* something that occurs or is brought about.

rick·et·y (rik′ ə tē) *adj.* shaky; about to fall apart or break down.

round up (round′ up′) *v.* to drive or herd something together, such as cattle or horses.

S

sash (sash) *n.* a broad band of cloth or ribbon worn around the waist or over one shoulder.

Sche·nec·ta·dy (skə nek′tə dē) *n.* a city in eastern New York.

scorn (skôrn) *n.* a feeling of hatred for someone or something thought of as bad or mean.

scut·tle (skut′ əl) *v.* **scut·tled, scut·tling.** to move with short, rapid steps.

sec·ond·hand (sek′ ənd hand′) *adj.* once owned or used by someone else.

se·lec·tion (si lek′ shən) *n.* a person or thing that is chosen.

ser·pent (sur′ pənt) *n.* **1.** a snake, especially a large or poisonous one. **2.** a kind of fireworks that resembles a snake when it explodes.

shal·low (shal′ ō) *adj.* not deep.

shoe·shine chair (shōō′shīn chār′) *n.* a chair on which to sit while having one's shoes shined.

sky blue (skī blōō) *adj.* warm, light blue, like the color of the clear sky.

slave (slāv) *n.* a person who is the property of another person.

slav·er·y (slā′ vər ē) *n.* the practice of owning slaves.

sol·emn (sol′ əm) *adj.* very serious; grave.

spi·der·y (spī′ dər ē) *adj.* resembling a spider or a spider's web; long and thin or delicate.

starch (stärch) *n.* any substance used to stiffen cloth.

state·ment (stāt′ mənt) *n.* something said.

steer (stēr) *n.* a bull, especially one raised for beef.

stern (sturn) *adj.* strict; harsh.

stur·dy (stur′ dē) *adj.* strong, hardy.

sub·ject (sub′ jikt) *n.* a person under the control or authority of another.

sub·urb (sub′ urb) *n.* a residential area close to or on the edge of a city.

sum·mon (sum′ ən) *v.* to send for or request the presence of.

swear (swār) *v.* **swore, sworn, swear·ing.** to make a solemn statement.

swore (swôr) *v.* See *swear.*

syc·a·more (sik′ ə môr′) *n.* a kind of tree that has smooth, brown bark that flakes off in thin layers, leaving patches on the trunk.

sycamore

T

tan·ge·rine (tan′ jə rēn′) *n.* a sweet, juicy, reddish-orange citrus fruit.

tax (taks) *n. pl.,* **taxes.** money paid by people for the support of the government.

threat·en (thret′ən) *v.* to say what will be done to injure or punish someone or something.

to·bac·co (tə bak′ ō) *n.* plant leaves that are used for smoking and chewing.

torch (tôrch) *n.* a flaming light, usually consisting of a stick of wood or some ·material soaked in a substance that will burn wound around the end of a stick.

trad·ing post (trād′ ing pōst) *n.* a store or station set up by a trader or trading company in a sparsely settled or frontier region, where the local people can obtain goods, often in exchange for local products.

Tri·na (trē′ nə)

tur·quoise (tur′ kwoiz, tur′ koiz) *n.* a greenish-blue stone.

U

un·der·brush (un′ dər brush′) *n.* bushes, shrubs, or other plants growing beneath large trees in a forest or woods.

un·ex·pect·ed (un′ iks pek′ tid) *adj.* unforeseen; coming or happening without warning.

V

vain (vān) *adj.* conceited; overly concerned with or proud of one's appearance, abilities, or accomplishments.

vi·sion (vizh′ ən) *n.* something that is imagined or dreamed.

W

wan·der (won′ dər) *v.* **1.** to go or move about aimlessly; roam. **2.** to go at a slow, relaxed pace; stroll.

---

a bad, ā cake, ä father; e pet, ē me; i it, i īce; o hot, ō open, ô off; oo wood, ōō food; oi oil, ou out; th thin, th that; u cup, ur turn, yōō music; zh treasure; ə ago, taken, pencil, lemon, helpful

weep (wēp) *v.* **wept, weep·ing.** to show strong emotion, such as joy or grief, by shedding tears.

wheel·chair (hwēl′ chār′, wel′ chār) *n.* a chair on wheels, used especially by people who cannot use their legs.

whim·per. (hwim′ pər, wim′ pər) *v.* to cry with weak, broken sounds.

wild·cat (wīld′ kat′) *n.* a wild animal of the cat family, such as the bobcat and the lynx.

wildcat

Y

year·ling (yēr′ ling) *n.* an animal that is one year old or in its second year.